동사

hear vs. listen

무슨 소리 났어? 나 못 들었는데.

중요한 거니까, 잘 들으세요.

I didn't ___________ that.

___________ carefully.

see vs. look

출근하다 보면 나는 많은 사람들을 봐.

정신 차려. 나를 쳐다봐.

I ___________ many people.

___________ at me.

say vs. tell

그는 "괜찮아?"라고 말했어.

그가 내게 예쁘다고 말했어.

He ___________ , "Are you okay?"

He ___________ me that I was pretty.

speak vs. talk

나 떨려. 나 내일 대중 앞에서 연설해야 해.

버스 타고 가면서 난 너와 이야기하는 거 좋아.

I have to ___________ in public.

I like ___________ to you.

wash vs. clean

머리가 가려워. 나 머리 감아야겠어.

정리 좀 하자. 테이블 치워줄 수 있니?

I ___________ to wash my hair.

Can you ___________ the table?

put on vs. wear

방에 들어가지 마. 그는 바지를 입고 있는 중이야.

나 어디 있는지 보여? 나 모자 쓰고 있어.

He's ___________ his pants.

I am ___________ a hat.

sit vs. seat

수업이 시작되어 그녀가 의자에 앉았어.

She _________ on a chair.

피곤해 보여서 내가 사람들을 바닥에 앉혔어.

I _________ people on the floor.

catch vs. hold

내가 더 빠르니까 난 너를 잡을 수 있어.

I can _________ you.

여기 너무 무서워. 내 손 잡아줄 수 있어?

can you _________ my hand?

sleep vs. go to bed

난 잠이 많거든. 난 10시간 자.

I _________ for 10 hours.

잘 자기 위해서 난 운동 후에 자러 가.

I _________ after exercising.

wake up vs. get up

엄마가 말했어. 아들, 잠에서 깰 시간이야.

It's time to _________, son.

소파에 앉아 있다가 그가 천천히 일어났어.

He _________ slowly.

walk vs. stroll

넌 뭐 해? 난 지금 걷는 중이야.

I'm _________ now.

머리가 복잡할 때 난 해변을 걸어.

I _________ on the beach.

travel vs. take a trip

다양한 문화를 좋아해서 그녀는 세계를 여행해.

She _________ the world.

너무 오래 앉아 있었다. 우리 정원에 가보자.

Let's _________ into my garden.

leave vs. depart

내일 아침 일정이 있어서 그는 파티에서 일찍 떠났어.

He _________ the party early.

출장 때문에 나 내일 런던으로 떠나.

I _________ for London tomrrow.

begin vs. start

시간 됐습니다. 시험 시작하세요.　　　　　______ our test.

준비되셨으면 시동 거세요.　　　　　______ your car.

finish vs. end

게임하기 전에 저녁식사를 끝내.　　　　　______ your dinner.

기나긴 전투 끝에 드디어 전쟁이 끝났어.　　　　　The war finally ______.

rent vs. borrow

결혼식 때 나 턱시도 빌릴 거야.　　　　　I'll ______ a tuxedo.

입을 옷이 없을 때 난 언니의 옷을 빌려.　　　　　I ______ my sister's clothes.

eat vs. have

난 닭껍질 안 먹어. 식감이 별로야.　　　　　I don't ______ chicken skin.

배고프다. 난 점심으로 피자 먹을 거야.　　　　　I'll ______ pizza for lunch.

gulp vs. sip

힘들어서 난 헬스장에서 물을 벌컥벌컥 마셔.　　　　　I ______ water at the gym.

커피가 뜨거워서 난 주로 커피를 홀짝여.　　　　　I usually ______ my coffee.

believe vs. trust

사람들이 뭐라고 해도 난 Tom이 옳다고 믿어.　　　　　I ______ Tom is right.

엄마는 항상 내 편이야. 난 엄마를 믿어.　　　　　I ______ my mom.

study vs. learn

문제를 풀거나 암기할 때 그녀는 집에서 공부해.　　　　　She ______ at home.

연설을 듣고 나서 나 교훈을 얻었어.　　　　　I ______ a lesson.

mix vs. blend

한번에 먹기 위해 난 그릇에 견과류를 섞어.　　I ________ nuts in a bowl.

소스를 만들기 위해서 난 재료를 섞었어.　　I ________ the ingredients.

stop vs. quit

밥 먹다가 전화 와서 그녀는 먹는 것을 멈췄어.　　She ________ eating.

건강에 해로워서 난 담배를 끊었어.　　I ________ smoking.

help vs. assist

여긴 위험하니까 아이들을 안전한 곳으로 가도록 도와.　　________ the children to safety.

수술실에서 간호사는 의사를 도와.　　The nurse ________ the doctor.

rest vs. relax

너무 피곤해서 난 퇴근 후 쉬었어.　　I ________ after work.

내년에 방콕에 가면 난 수영장에서 쉴 거야.　　I'm going to ________ in the pool.

fight vs. argue

좀 다쳤어. 나 어제 친구와 싸웠어.　　I ________ with my friend yesterday.

그들은 날 이해 못 해. 난 그들과 언쟁하지 않을 거야.　　I won't ________ with them.

hit vs. beat

정말 미안해. 너를 때릴 의도는 아니었어.　　I didn't mean to ________ you.

병원 가야 해. 그들이 어제 나를 구타했어.　　They ________ me yesterday.

laugh vs. smile

내가 생각할 때 난 잘 웃어.　　I ________ a lot.

그를 보면 그는 항상 웃고 있어.　　He's always ________.

cry vs. sob

| 난 어른이잖아. 난 더 이상 울지 않아. | I don't _______ anymore. |
| 엄마한테 혼나서 내 동생은 훌쩍거려. | My brother _______. |

delete vs. erase

| 컴퓨터에서 안 보여. 너 그 폴더 삭제했어? | Did you _______ the folder? |
| 부탁이 있어. 날 위해 칠판을 지워줄래? | Can you _______ the board for me? |

change vs. exchange

| 차가 자꾸 고장 나. 나 차 바꿀 거야. | I'll _______ my car. |
| 인사 후 우리는 명함을 교환했어. | We _______ business cards. |

blink vs. wink

| 눈에 뭐가 들어갔나 봐. 그는 눈을 깜빡이고 있어. | He's _______. |
| 얘기할 게 있어. 그가 나에게 윙크했어. | He _______ at me. |

fix vs. repair

| 싱크대에 물이 새서 그는 테이프를 붙여 고쳤어. | He _______ it with tape. |
| 카센터에 차를 가져갔는데 그가 엔진을 고쳤어. | He _______ the engine. |

hurt vs. injure

| 자꾸 때리지 마. 날 아프게 하지 마. | Don't _______ me. |
| 어제 친구들이랑 놀다가 나 다리를 부상당했어. | I _______ my legs. |

collect vs. gather

| 기회가 될 때마다 난 게임을 모아. | I _______ games. |
| 겨울을 대비하기 위해 그녀는 장작을 모았어. | She _______ firewood. |

remember vs. recall

항상 나에게 친절했거든. 난 그녀를 잘 기억하지.
잘 생각해봐. 너 그의 이름을 기억해?

I _________ her well.
Do you _________ his name?

chop vs. slice

카레에 넣으려고 난 당근을 잘랐어.
샌드위치에 넣을 거라서 난 토마토를 얇게 썰었어.

I _________ some carrots.
I _________ a tomato.

save vs. store

다 수정했어. 이 파일 어떻게 저장하면 돼?
책이 너무 많아서 난 내 책들을 지하실에 보관해.

How can I _________ this file?
I _________ my books in the basement.

choose vs. select

고민 끝에 거절하기로 결정했어.
계속 진행하시려면 목록에서 하나를 선택하세요.

I _________ to say no.
Please _________ one from the list.

make vs. create

배고파서 난 라면을 끓였어.
타고난 천재성으로 그는 전기를 만들었어.

I _________ ramen.
He _________ electricity.

move vs. carry

방이 바뀌어서 난 내 짐을 모두 옮겼어.
정말 궁금한데 비둘기가 질병을 옮겨?

I _________ all my stuff.
Do pigeons _________ diseases?

teach vs. instruct

초등학교에서 난 그들에게 덧셈을 가르쳤어.
시험 보기 전에 난 그들에게 규칙을 가르쳐줬어.

I _________ them addition.
I _________ them on the rules.

increse vs. raise

수지가 안 맞아서 주인이 가격을 올렸어.

질문이 있어서 그녀는 손을 들었어.

The owner _________ the price.

She _________ her hand.

arrive vs. reach

걱정 마. 그녀는 8시 30분에 도착했어.

노력 끝에 난 목적을 달성했어.

She _________ at 8:30 p.m.

I _________ my goal.

slide vs. slip

썰매 타는 사람들이 눈 위에서 미끄러지고 있어.

물청소 했거든. 바닥이 젖었어. 미끄러지지 마.

People are _________ on the snow.

The floor is wet. Don't _________.

push vs. nudge

너는 목록을 확인해. 난 카트를 밀게.

TV 보는데 그가 나를 쿡 찌르며 말을 걸었어.

I'll _________ the cart.

He _________ me and talked to me.

breathe vs. pant

이제 정신이 들어? 숨 쉴 수 있어?

공원에서 뛰었더니 우리 개들이 헐떡이고 있어.

Can you _________ ?

My dogs are _________.

turn vs. spin

빛이 반사돼서 난 거울을 돌렸어.

넌 손가락으로 공 돌릴 수 있어?

I _________ the mirror.

Can you _________ a ball on your finger?

join vs. sign up

재밌겠다. 나도 껴도 돼?

메시지 받은 후 난 멤버십에 가입했어.

Can I _________ you?

I _________ for a membership.

hate vs. dislike

친구들이 괴롭히나 봐. 그는 학교 가는 걸 싫어해.

난 커피를 좋아하지 않아. 너무 써.

He __________ going to school.

I __________ coffee.

barbecue vs. grill

장작 가져가. 해변에서 음식을 구울 수 있대.

We can __________ the food on the beach.

햄버거에 넣으려고 난 양파를 석쇠에 구웠어.

I __________ some onions.

SECTION 2

명사

rest vs. break

제가 지병이 있는데 한 달 동안 쉬어도 될까요?
너무 오래 회의했네. 우리 5분 쉬어도 될까요?

Can I take a __________ for a month?
Can we take a five minute __________?

floor vs. story

잘 찾아오고 있어? 방은 3층에 있어.

지금 보여드릴 집은 2층짜리 집입니다.

The room is on the third __________.

It'is a two __________ house.

fee vs. fare

성인 2명인데 입장료가 얼만가요?
다행이다. 중국에서 버스 요금은 비싸지 않아.

How much is the admission __________?
The bus __________ isn't expensive in China.

looks vs. appearance

진짜 너무 부럽다. 그녀는 예뻐.

그를 왜 좋아하냐고? 그의 외모가 좋아.

She has good ___________.

I like his ___________.

house vs. home

나는 방 3개짜리 집이 있어.

여기 너무 편해. 집 같은 느낌이야.

I have a three bedroom ___________.

I feel ___________.

taste vs. flavor

난 커피 안 좋아해. 커피는 쓴맛이 나.

먹어봤어? 육개장은 깊은 맛이 나.

Coffee has a bitter ___________.

육개장 has a rich ___________.

customer vs. client

여기 매일 오셔. 그녀는 나의 단골 손님이거든.

유능한 변호사인가 봐. 그는 고객이 많아.

She's my ___________ customer.

He has many ___________.

medicine vs. drug

몸 생각해서 먹어. 좋은 약은 입에 써.

그는 약에 대해 잘 알아. 그는 제약회사에서 일하거든.

A good ___________ tastes bitter.

He works for a ___________ company.

baggage vs. bag

1박 2일 여행 가는데 너 짐이 너무 많다.

이제 갈 건가 봐. 그는 가방을 싸고 있어.

You have a lot of ___________.

He's packing his ___________.

tour vs. journey

저 신입생인데요, 캠퍼스 투어 할 수 있을까요?

건강관리 잘해. 우리는 긴 여정을 앞두고 있어.

Can I have a campus ___________?

We have a long ___________ ahead.

salary vs. wage

기분 좋다. 사장님이 내 월급을 올려주셨어.
돈을 좀 더 모아야 해. 그의 주급은 100달러야.

My boss raised my __________.
His weekly __________ are $100.

photo vs. picture

정말 멋지다. 이거 최근 사진이니?
이 책은 그림이 많아. 그래서 이해가 잘돼.

Is that a recent __________?
This book has many __________.

store vs. shop

뭐 필요한 거 없어? 나 지금 편의점에 갈 건데.

직장을 그만두고 그녀는 네일숍을 열었어.

I'm going to a convenience __________.

She opened a nail __________.

bathroom vs. restroom

집이 참 좋다. 근데 화장실 좀 써도 되니?
혹시 필요하다면 화장실은 복도 건너편에 있어.

Can I use your __________?
The __________ is across the hall.

signature vs. autograph

고객님! 여기에 서명이 필요합니다.
저 팬인데요, 사인받을 수 있나요?

I need your __________ here.
Can I get your __________?

trash vs. garbage

쓰레기를 보면 우리는 쓰레기를 주워야 해.
며칠 전에 음식물 쓰레기 버렸니?

We need to pick up the __________.
Did you take out the __________?

road vs. street

난 길을 따라 호수로 갔어. 풍경이 좋더라고.
넌 길가에서 많은 상점들을 볼 수 있어.

I followed the __________ to the lake.
You can see many stores on the __________.

manners vs. etiquette

장점을 말하자면 내 남자친구는 매너가 좋아.
미리 읽어주세요. 10가지 사무실 에티켓이 있습니다.

My boyfriend has good ___________.
There're 10 office ___________ rules.

chance vs. opportunity

정말 운이 좋아. 난 발표할 기회를 얻었거든.

지금까지 노력했잖아. 너의 기회를 놓치지 마.

I got a _________ to show my presentation.
Don't miss your _________.

exam vs. test

이제 홀가분하다. 나 시험 모두 잘 봤어.
혈액형을 몰라. 나 피검사 받아야 돼.

I did well on all my ___________.
I have to take a blood _________.

cuisine vs. dish

매운 거 좋아해? 인도 요리는 살짝 매워.
결정이 힘드시면 주방장 특선 요리를 추천할게요.

Indian _________ is a little spicy.
I recommend the chef's _________.

buddy vs. mate

왜 혼자 있어? 너 친구는 어디 있니, 아들아?
걱정하지 마. 나 지금 반 친구랑 같이 있어.

Where's your _________, son?
I'm with my class _________ now.

company vs. party

어서 오세요. 일행 있으세요?
예약 부탁 드려요. 저희는 3명이에요.

Do you have _________ ?
We're a _______ of 3.

seasoning vs. spice

좀 싱거워. 우리 양념을 더 넣어야겠다.
후추, 생강, 계피는 향신료야.

We need to add more _________.
Pepper, ginger, and cinnamon are _________.

meal vs. snack

건강을 생각해서 난 하루에 3끼를 먹어.

출출하네. 간식 생각 있니?

I have three ___________ a day.

Do you feel like having a ___________?

movie vs. film

난 로맨스 영화를 좋아해.

기대해도 좋아. 그것은 국제 영화 축제야.

I like romance ________.

It's an international ________ festival.

letter vs. characte

이거 P야 R이야? 이 글자 알아보겠니?

한자를 읽을 줄 알아?

Can you recognize this ___________?

Do you know how to read Chinese ___________?

sea vs. ocean

아이들 좀 봐. 그들은 바다에서 수영하고 있어.

이 강은 태평양으로 흘러 들어가.

They're swimming in the ________.

This river flows into the Pacific ________.

knee vs. lap

의사 선생님, 제가 무릎을 구부릴 수가 없어요.

귀엽지? 우리 개가 내 허벅지 위에 앉아 있어.

I can't bend my ________.

My dog is sitting on my ________.

prize vs. award

시합에 나갈지 말지 고민이야. 우승자 상이 뭐야?

내 곡이 히트를 쳤어. 나 내 음악으로 상 받았어.

What's the winner's ________?

I got an ________ for my music.

heaven vs. paradise

어제 나 그 소식 듣고 기분이 끝내줬거든.

나 하와이에 일주일 있었거든. 지상 낙원이었어.

I was in ___________ at the news.

It was ___________.

child vs. kid

난 작가예요. 난 어린아이들 책을 써요.

I'm writing a book for young ____________.

성숙해 보이지만 그는 아직 애야.

He's just a ____________.

class vs. lesson

이젠 여유로워. 나 이번 학기에 수업 2개 들어.

I'm taking two ____________ this semester.

TV 보다가 나 노래 개인 레슨에 늦었어.

I was late for my singing ____________.

bonus vs. incentive

기분 좋겠다. 직원들이 크리스마스 보너스 받았거든.

The staff got a Christmas ____________.

우리 회사는 장려책으로 여행을 시켜줘.

My company offers a trip as an ____________.

advertisement vs. commercial

그 시계, 나 잡지에서 그 광고 봤어.

I saw the ____________ in a magazine.

채널 고정! 광고 후에 돌아오겠습니다.

We'll be right back after the ____________.

clothes vs. clothing

난 집 도착하면 옷 갈아입어.

I change my ____________ when I get home.

그들은 의류, 신발, 액세서리를 팔아.

They sell ____________, shoes, and accessories.

stairs vs. step

엘리베이터 고장 났어. 계단으로 가자.

Let's take the ____________.

카페 분위기 좋아. 밖에 돌계단도 있어.

There're some stone ____________ outside.

plate vs. dish

부탁이 있는데 난 접시 2개가 더 필요해.

I need two more ____________.

실례합니다. 비누 그릇이 어디 있나요?

Where's the soap ____________?

package vs. packet

무겁네. 상자 드는 거 도와줄 수 있니?

게임 시작하자. 카드 한 곽 열어줄래?

Can you help me lift the __________?

Can you open a __________ of cards?

homework vs. assignment

숙제 못 했어. 숙제하다가 잠들었거든.

교수님 말씀을 놓쳤어. 오늘 역사 과제가 뭐야?

I fell asleep while I was doing my __________.

What's today's __________ in history?

chef vs. cook

그는 런던 호텔 전문 요리사로 취직했거든.

우리 엄마는 요리를 잘해.

He took a job as a __________ in a London hotel.

My mom is a good __________.

center vs. middle

단팥빵 먹을 때 난 빵 가운데 먹는 걸 좋아해.

말 시키지 마. 나 지금 뭐 하고 있어.

I love to eat the __________ of the bread.

I'm in the __________ of something her

page vs. sheet

다 읽었으면 다음 장으로 넘기세요.

편지 써야겠다. 종이 한 장이 필요해.

Please turn to the nex __________.

I need a __________ of paper.

carpet vs. rug

따뜻해. 바닥에 아늑한 카펫이 깔려 있어.

샤워한 후에 깔개에 발 닦으렴.

The floor is covered with a cozy __________.

Wipe your feet on the __________.

error vs. mistake

윈도우10을 깔았는데 내 컴퓨터에 오류 났어.

영어가 어렵지만 넌 철자를 너무 많이 틀리네.

My computer gave me an __________.

You make too many spelling __________.

thought vs. idea

편안하게 해주었더니 그는 자유롭게 그의 생각들을 말했다. He spoke his ＿＿＿＿＿ freely.

새로운 사업을 할 거야. 내 생각은 빵집을 여는 거야. My ＿＿＿＿＿ is to open a bakery.

place vs. area

우리 집엔 손님 계시니까 내가 너네 집으로 갈게. I'll come to your ＿＿＿＿＿.

들어오시면 안 돼요. 여기는 제한 구역입니다. This is a restricted ＿＿＿＿＿.

stone vs. rock

아름답지? 루비는 보석의 한 종류야. Ruby is a type of precious ＿＿＿＿＿.

산에서 도망가다 그는 큰 바위 뒤에 몸을 숨겼어. He hid himself behind a large ＿＿＿＿＿.

woman vs. female

일하는 여성들의 수가 증가하고 있어. The number of working ＿＿＿＿＿ is increasing.

예쁘지? 우리 강아지는 암컷이야. My dog is a ＿＿＿＿＿.

boat vs. ship

재밌겠다. 그들은 작은 배에서 낚시하고 있어. They're fishing on the tiny ＿＿＿＿＿.

이번 휴가 때 난 배 타고 하와이 갈 거야. I'm going to Hawaii by ＿＿＿＿＿.

형용사·부사

small vs. little

경기가 안 좋아서 많은 소기업들이 파산했어.

Many _________ companies went bankrupt.

장보러 가야지. 우유가 조금밖에 안 남았어.

There's only a _________ milk left.

all vs. every

몽땅 버려야겠어. 달걀이 다 썩었어.

이 사전의 단어 하나하나 모두 중요해.

_________ the eggs went bad.

_________ word in this dictionary is important.

tall vs. high

너도 조심해. 키 큰 사람들은 종종 허리 통증이 있어.

발이 아프지만 많은 여성들이 하이힐을 신어.

_________ people often get backaches.

Many women wear _________ heels.

so vs. too

정말 고마워. 이거 굉장히 로맨틱하다.

다른 길로 가자. 차가 다니기에 길이 너무 좁아.

This is _________ romantic.

The road is _________ narrow for cars.

quick vs. fast

이거 급한 거야. 넌 신속한 결정을 내려야 해.

난 타수가 느려. 그녀는 타이핑이 굉장히 빨라.

You have to make a _________ decision.

She's a very _________ typist.

lonely vs. alone

난 더 이상 외로움을 느끼고 싶지 않아.

협업보다는 난 혼자 일하는 것을 선호해.

I don't want to be _________ anymore.

I prefer working _________.

no vs. not

더 기다려. 아무 결정도 내려지지 않았어.   ________ decisions have been made.

사업해요. 저는 회사원이 아니에요.   I'm ________ an office worker.

ago vs. before

참 오래됐네. 이 사진은 20년 전에 찍은 거야.   This photo was taken 20 years ________.

서둘러야 해. 월요일 전에 할 수 있을까?   Can we do it ________ Monday?

smooth vs. soft

평온하다. 바다 표면이 유리처럼 잔잔하네.   The sea was as ________ as glass.

우리 할머니는 부드러운 음식만 드셔.   My grandma can only eat ________ food.

clean vs. clear

5성급은 좋더라. 호텔 방이 매우 깨끗했어.   The hotel room was very ________.

잔이 예쁘다. 이 와인 잔은 굉장히 투명해.   This wine glass is very ________.

electric vs. electronic

좀 춥네. 전기 히터 전원 좀 꽂아줄래?   Can you plug in the ________ heater?

이북은 전자 책을 의미해.   E-book means an ________ book.

last vs. final

학생 여러분, 마지막 문장을 읽을 수 있나요?   Can you read the ________ sentence?

더 이상은 안 돼. 이게 나의 최종 제안이야.   This is my ________ offer.

slim vs. skinny

패션쇼 갔었는데 그 모델은 몸매가 날씬했어.   The model had a very ________ figure.

비현실적이야. 어떤 슈퍼모델들은 굉장히 말랐어.   Some supermodels are far too ________.

sometime vs. sometimes

연락해. 언제 한번 보자.
그거 아니? 가끔씩 네가 이상해.

Let's get together ___________.
You're strange ___________.

a little vs. a few

간이 안 맞네. 너 소금 좀 더 넣어야겠다.

출장 때문에 그는 가방에 몇 가지 물건들을 넣었어.

You need to put in _________ more salt.
He packed _________ things into a ba

ripe vs. mature

다른 걸로 사자. 이 토마토들은 아직 안 익었네.
대화를 나눠보면 그녀는 나이에 비해 성숙해.

These tomatoes aren't _________ yet.
She's _________ for her age.

childlike vs. childish

그가 어린아이 같은 눈으로 나를 봤어.

죄송하지만 그건 좀 유치한 거 같아요.

He looked at me with ___________ eyes.
I think that is a little ___________.

shy vs. ashamed

기대하지 마. 그는 부끄러워서 여자한테 말도 못 걸어.
그런 잘못을 해놓고 너는 스스로 부끄럽지도 않니?

He is too _________ to talk to girls.
Aren't you _________ of yourself?

flat vs. even

운동을 좋아해서 아이들을 안전한 곳으로 가도록 도와.
웃을 때 예뻐. 간호사는 의사를 도와.

She has a _________ stomach.
She has _________ teeth.

hard vs. difficult

30년을 함께 살아서 난 퇴근 후 쉬었어.
컴퓨터 고치는 거 어려울 거야.

The divorce was _________ on them.
Fixing the computer is going to be ___________.

sick vs. ill

일을 못 끝냈어. 나 이번 달에 병가를 10일 냈었거든.

그녀는 매우 아팠고 최근에 돌아가셨어.

I took ten _________ days this month.

She was very _________ and recently passed away.

clever vs. smart

이런 생각을 떠올리다니 정말 영리한걸!

안경 쓰니까 너 오늘 똑똑해 보인다.

How _________ of you to think of this idea.

You look very _________ today.

big vs. large

BTS 사랑해요. 난 당신의 광팬이에요.

햄버거가 큰데 콜라 큰 사이즈로 드릴까요?

I'm a _________ fan of yours.

Would you like a _________ coke with that?

sweet vs. friendly

너도 들어봐. 그녀의 다정한 목소리가 좋지 않니?

이 식당 또 오자. 여기 웨이터들이 참 친절해.

Don't you love her _________ voice?

The waiters here are so _________.

wide vs. broad

강이 넓어서 난 뛰어넘을 수가 없어.

그는 키가 크고 어깨가 넓어.

The river is so _________ I can't jump over it.

He's tall with _________ shoulders.

complex vs. complicated

이 그림을 봐. 인간의 뇌구조는 복잡해.

난 생각이 달라. 사랑은 복잡하지 않아.

The map of the human brain is _________.

Love isn't _________.

famous vs. popular

이 식당은 프랑스 요리로 잘 알려져 있어.

새우는 인기 있는 해산물 종류예요.

This restaurant is _________ for its French cuisine.

Shrimps are a _________ type of seafood.

valuable vs. precious

자주 먹자. 아보카도는 소중한 음식이야.
영상 지우지 마. 추억은 소중한 거야.

The avocado is a __________ food.
Memories are __________ .

really vs. very

장난 아니야. 그들은 진짜 쌍둥이라고.
와, 너 사무실 굉장히 잘 정리돼 있다.

They're __________ twins.
Wow, your office is __________ organized.

terrible vs. horrible

거기 가지 마. 그 식당 음식 정말 끔찍해.

자다 깼어. 나 어젯밤 무시무시한 꿈을 꿨거든.

They serve __________ food at that restaurant.
I had a __________ dream last night.